EASIEST 5-FIN
PIANO COLLEC

GW00383768

Popular Jazz Standards

15 well-known jazz standards
arranged for 5-finger piano

Wise Publications
part of The Music Sales Group
London / New York / Paris / Sydney / Copenhagen / Berlin / Madrid / Tokyo

I'M OLD FASHIONED

Words by Johnny Mercer
Music by Jerome Kern

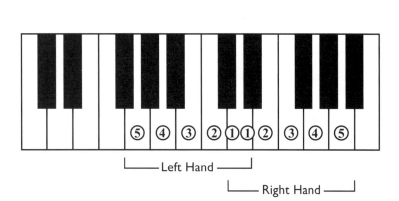

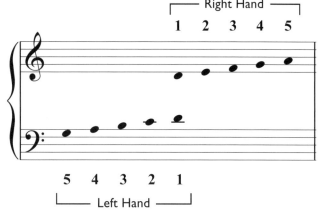

Steadily and tenderly ♩ = 104

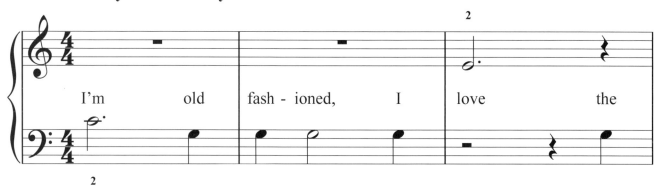

I'm old fash-ioned, I love the

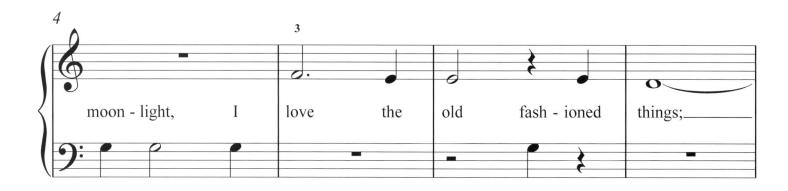

moon-light, I love the old fash-ioned things;

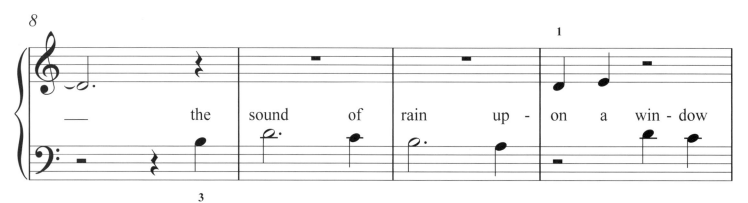

the sound of rain up-on a win-dow

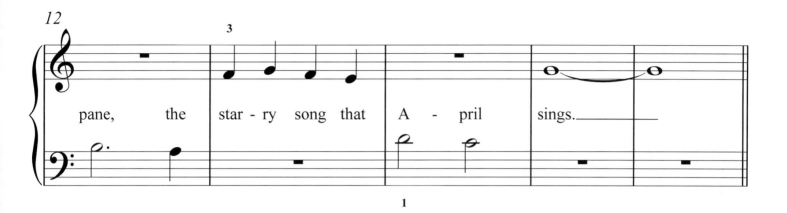

pane, the star - ry song that A - pril sings.

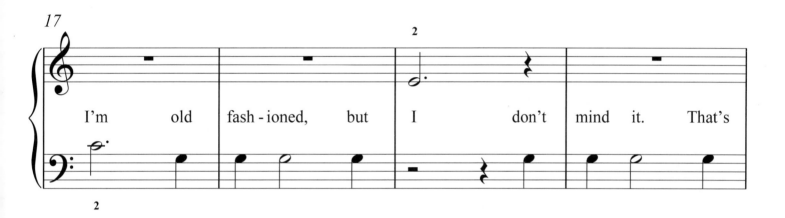

I'm old fash - ioned, but I don't mind it. That's

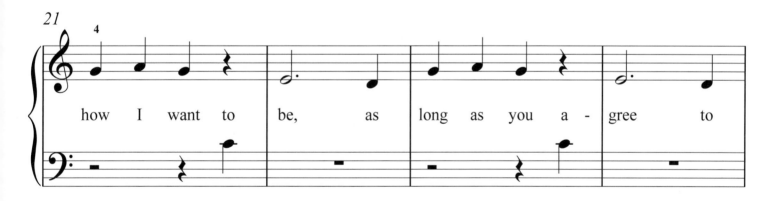

how I want to be, as long as you a - gree to

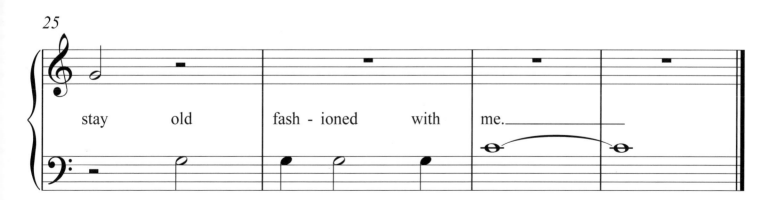

stay old fash - ioned with me.

SOLITUDE

Words by Eddie De Lange & Irving Mills
Music by Duke Ellington

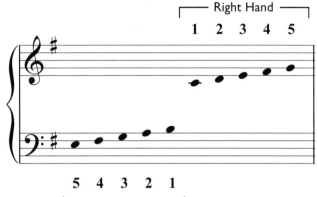

Sadly ♩ = 72

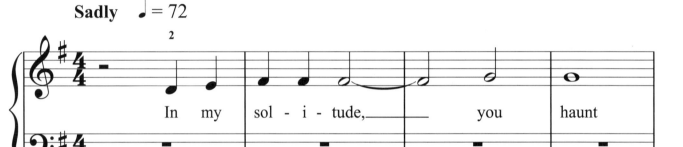

In my sol - i - tude, you haunt

me with rev - er - ies of days gone by.

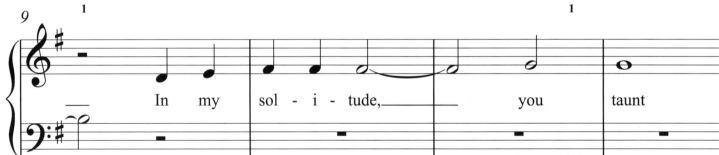

In my sol - i - tude, you taunt

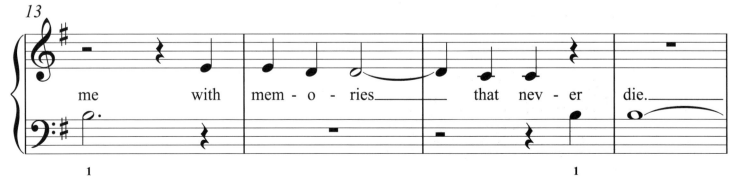

me with mem - o - ries that nev - er die.

I sit in my chair, I'm filled with des - pair; there's

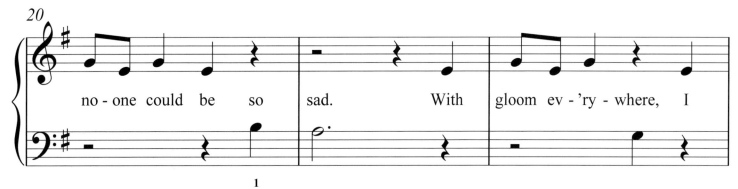

no - one could be so sad. With gloom ev - 'ry - where, I

sit and I stare. I know that I'll soon go mad. In my

sol - i - tude,_____ I'm pray - ing, "Dear

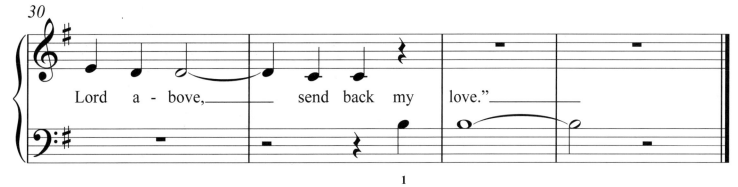

Lord a - bove,_____ send back my love."_____

OVER THE RAINBOW

Words by E.Y. Harburg
Music by Harold Arlen

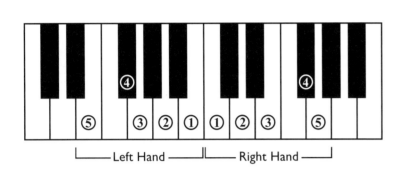

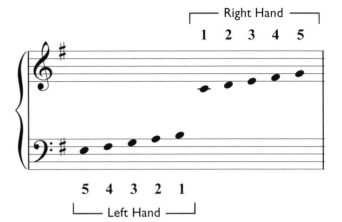

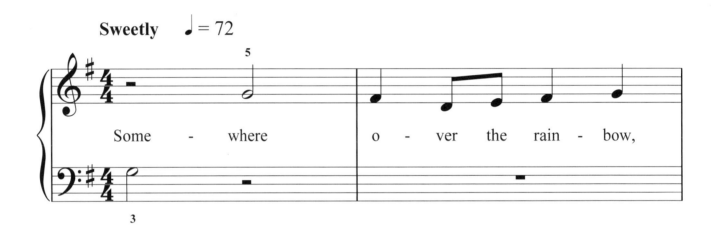

Some - where   o - ver the rain - bow,

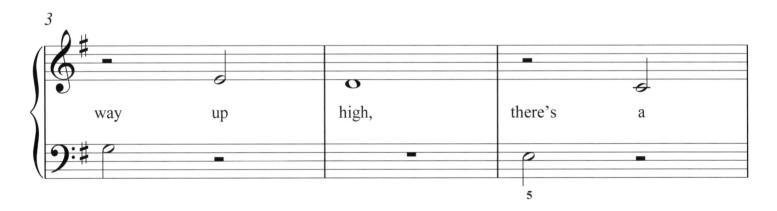

way   up   high,   there's   a

land   that   I   heard   of   once   in   a   lul - la - by.

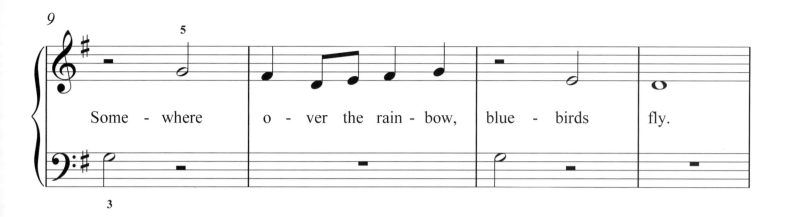

Some - where   o - ver the rain - bow,   blue - birds   fly.

Birds   fly   o - ver the rain - bow,   why   then, oh   why   can't

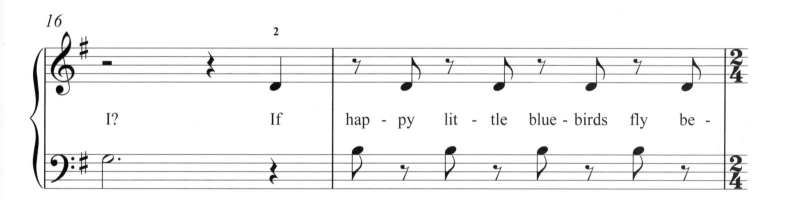

I?   If   hap - py   lit - tle   blue - birds   fly   be -

- yond   the rain - bow,   why,   oh   why   can't   I?

THE WAY YOU LOOK TONIGHT

Words by Dorothy Fields
Music by Jerome Kern

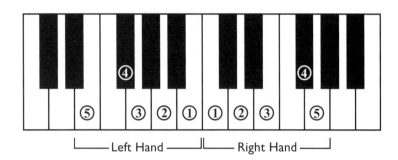

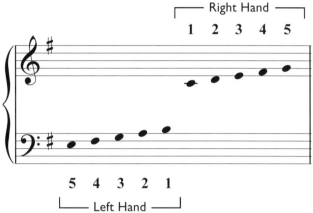

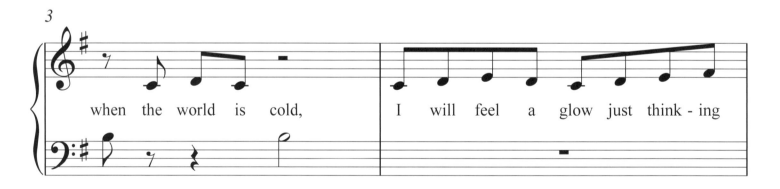

Oh, but you're love - ly, nev - er, ev - er change,

keep that breath-less charm, won't you please ar - range it, 'cause I

love you just the way you look to - night.

Just the way you look to - night.

SUMMERTIME

Music by George Gershwin

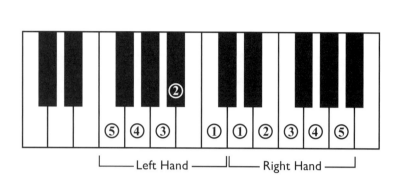

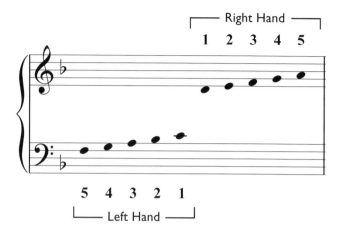

Steady swing ♩ = 80

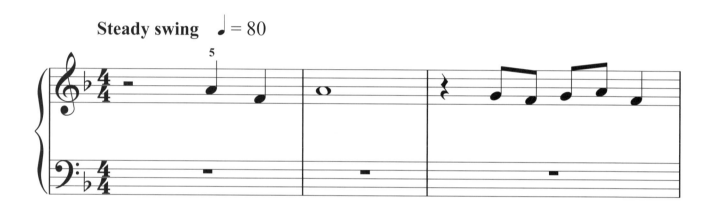

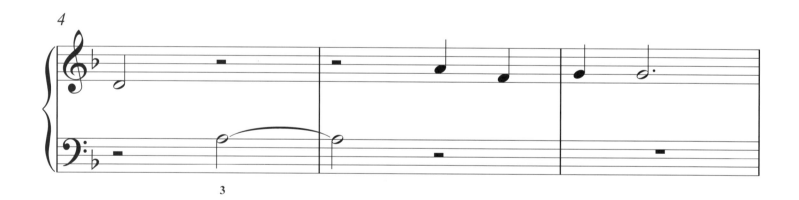

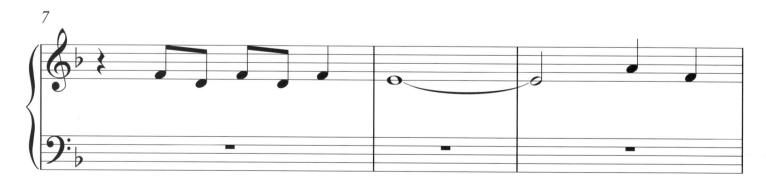

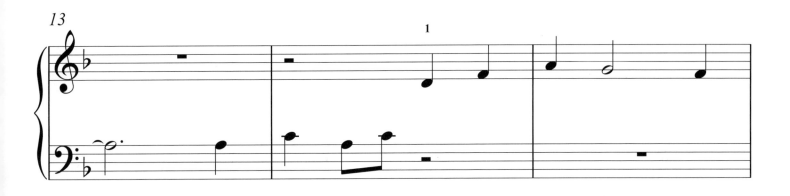

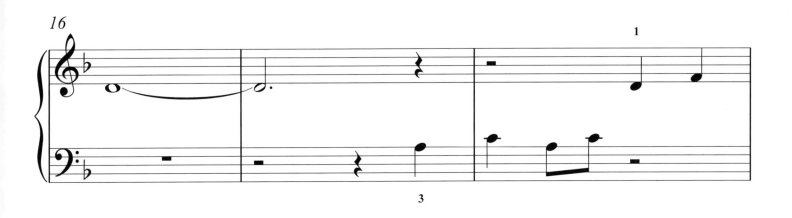

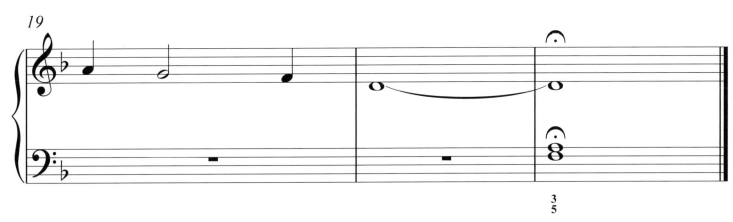

HONEYSUCKLE ROSE

Words by Andy Razaf
Music by Fats Waller

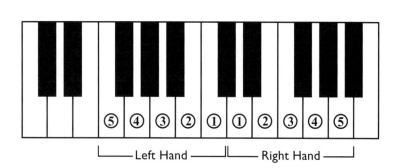

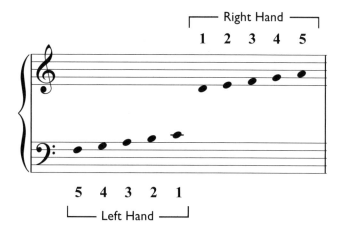

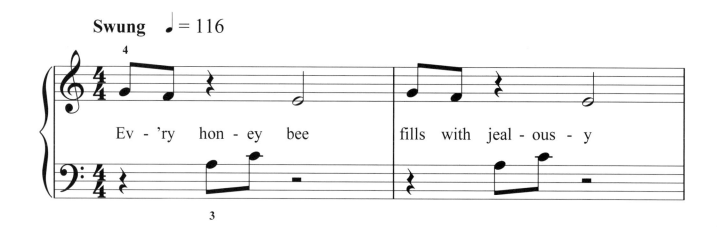

Ev - 'ry hon - ey bee fills with jeal - ous - y

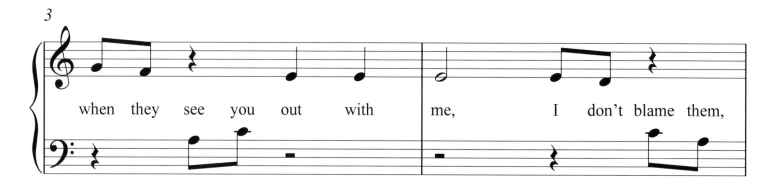

when they see you out with me, I don't blame them,

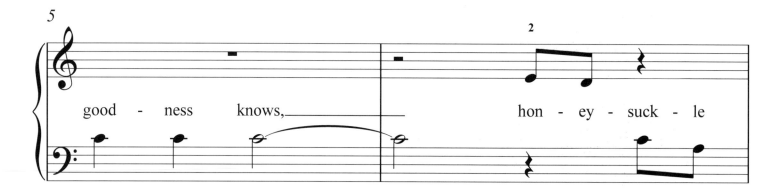

good - ness knows, hon - ey - suck - le

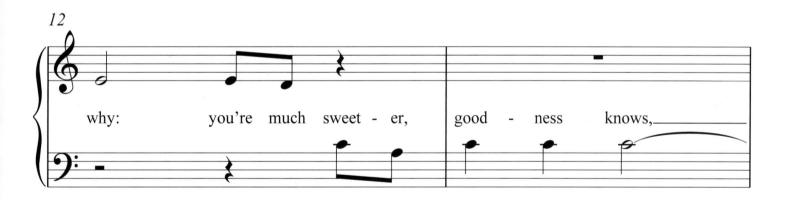

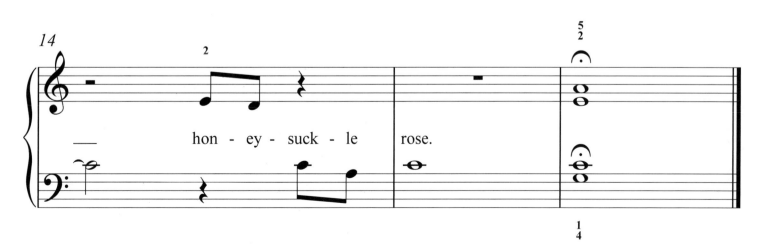

THESE FOOLISH THINGS

Words by Eric Maschwitz
Music by Jack Strachey

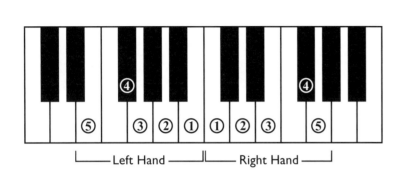

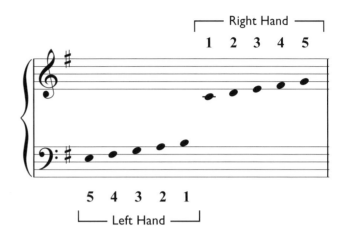

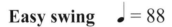

Easy swing ♩ = 88

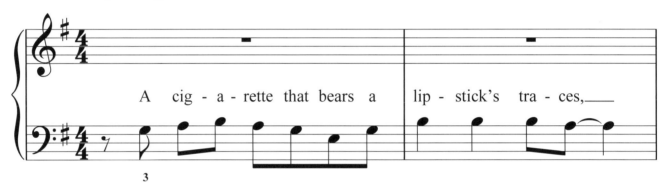

A cig - a - rette that bears a lip - stick's tra - ces,____

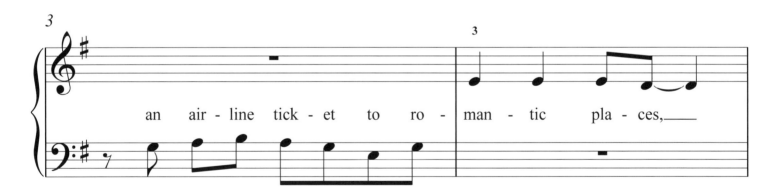

an air - line tick - et to ro - man - tic pla - ces,____

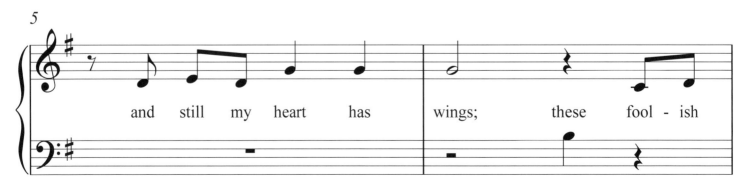

and still my heart has wings; these fool - ish

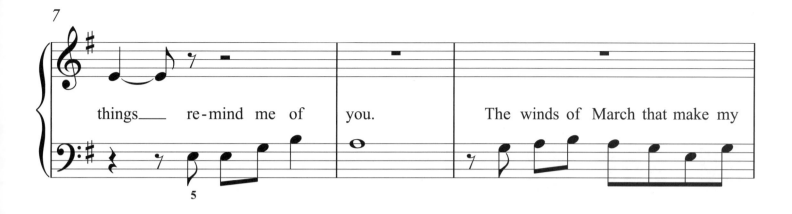

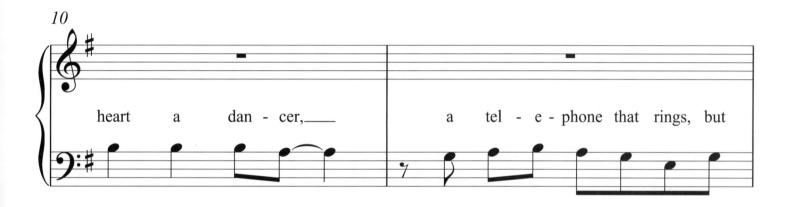

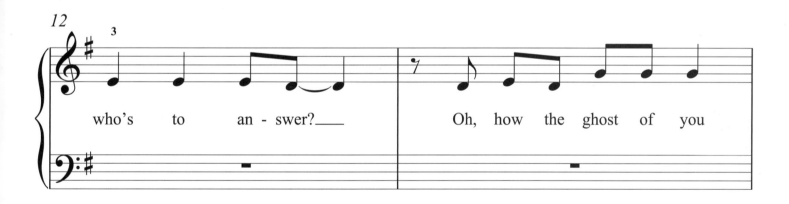

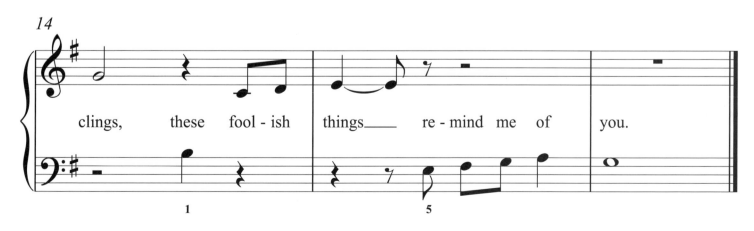

THE VERY THOUGHT OF YOU

Words & Music by Ray Noble

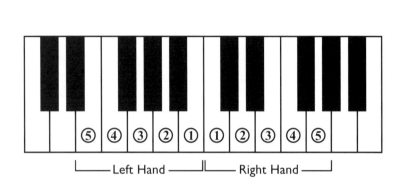

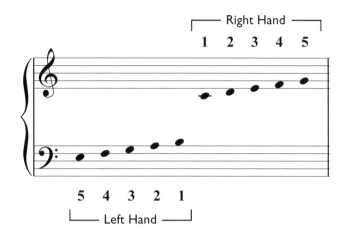

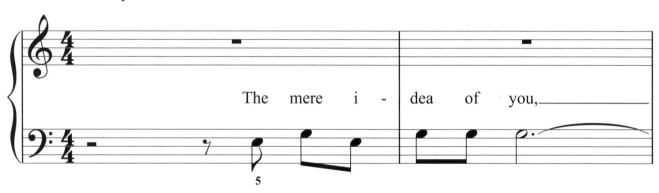

The mere i - dea of you, and I for - get to do

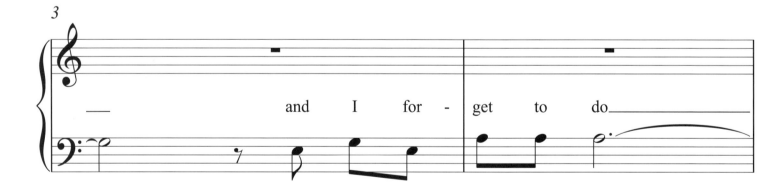

the lit - tle or - di - nar - y

SUNNY

Words & Music by Bobby Hebb

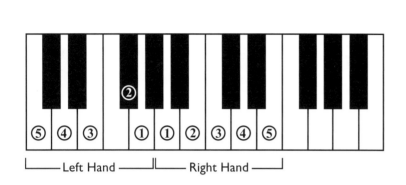

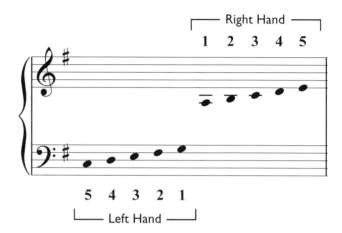

Energetically, with a bounce ♩ = 116

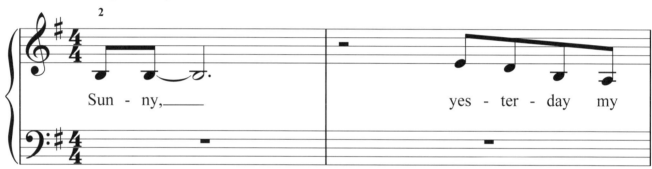

Sun - ny,＿＿＿ yes - ter - day my

life was filled with rain.＿ Sun - ny,＿

you smiled at me and real - ly eased the pain.＿

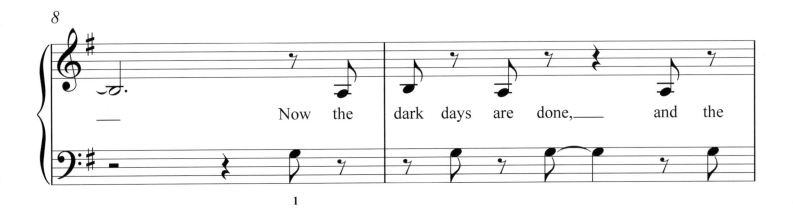

Now the dark days are done,___ and the

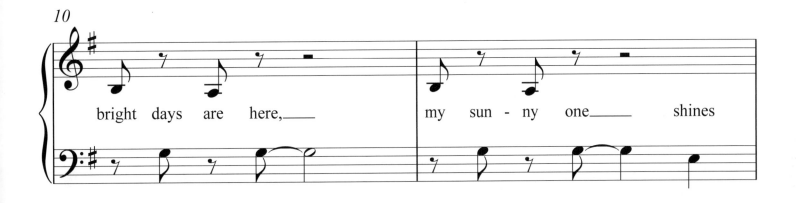

bright days are here,___ my sun - ny one___ shines

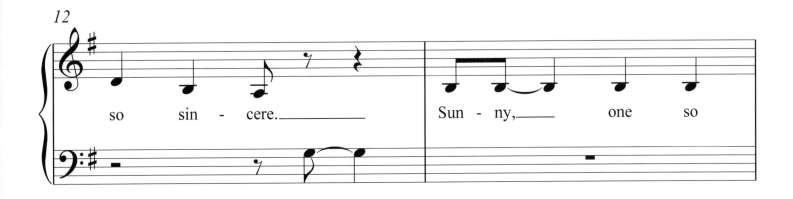

so sin - cere.___ Sun - ny,___ one so

true, I love___ you.___

SOMEONE TO WATCH OVER ME

Music by George Gershwin

PERDIDO

Words by Ervin Drake & Harry Lenk
Music by Juan Tizol

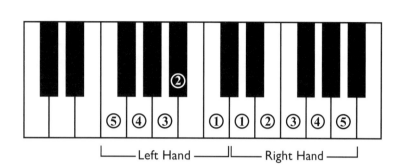

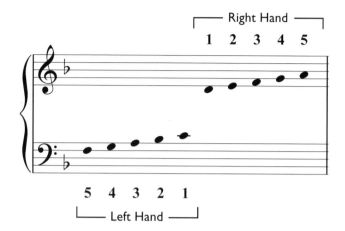

Lazy swing ♩ = 112

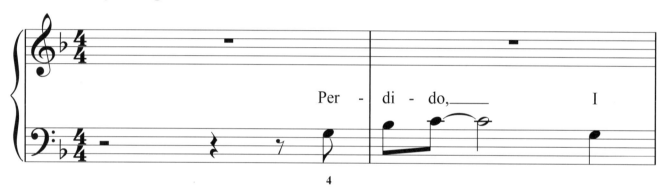

chanc - ing a dance fi - es - ta.____ Per -

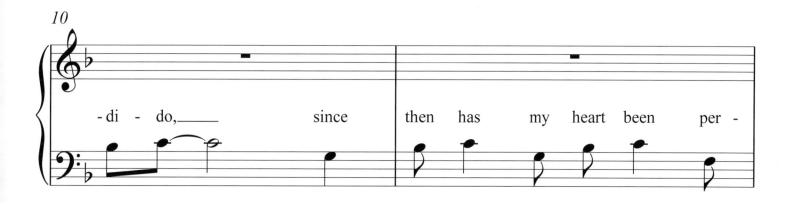

-di - do,____ since then has my heart been per -

-di - do.___ I know I must go to Tor - ri - do,____ that

yearn - ing to lose Per - di - do.____

IT DON'T MEAN A THING (IF IT AIN'T GOT THAT SWING)

Words by Irving Mills
Music by Duke Ellington

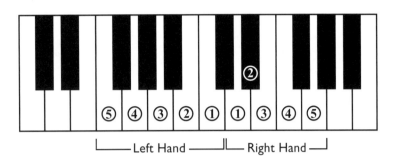

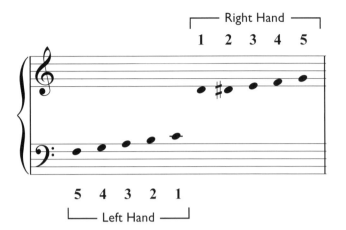

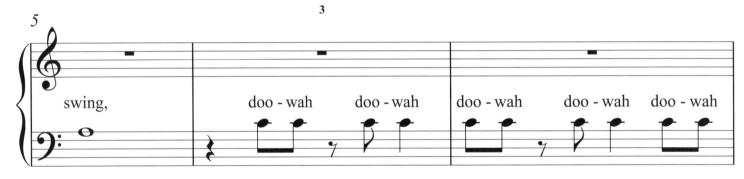

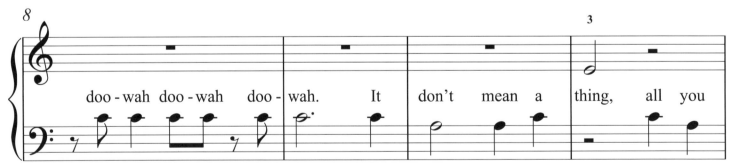

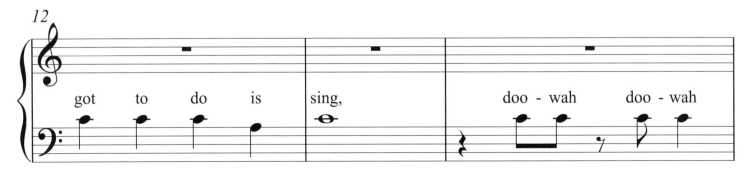

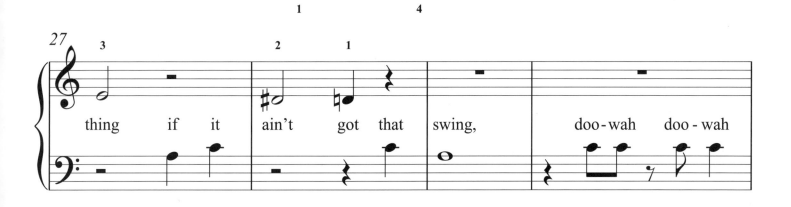

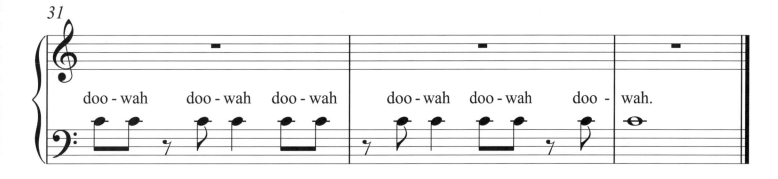

ST THOMAS

Music by Sonny Rollins

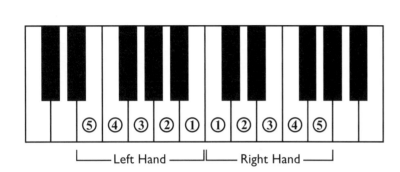

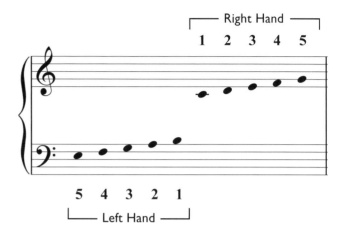

With a Latin feel ♩ = 168

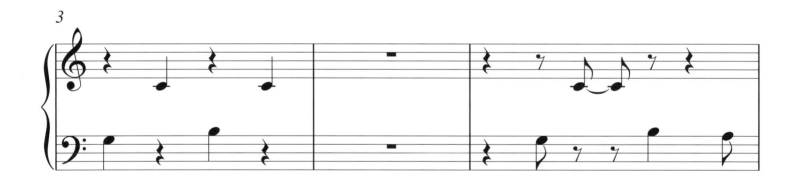

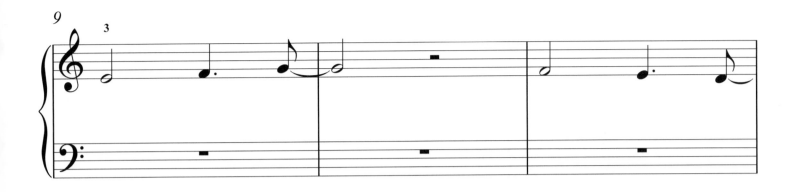

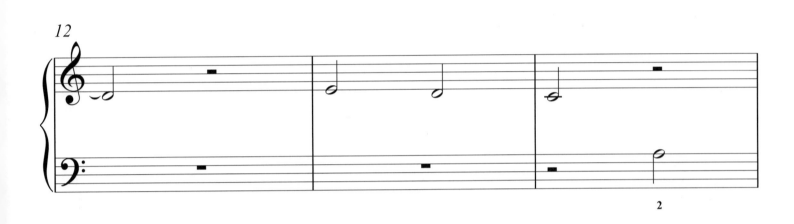

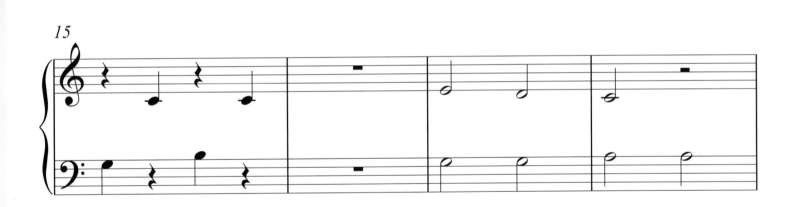

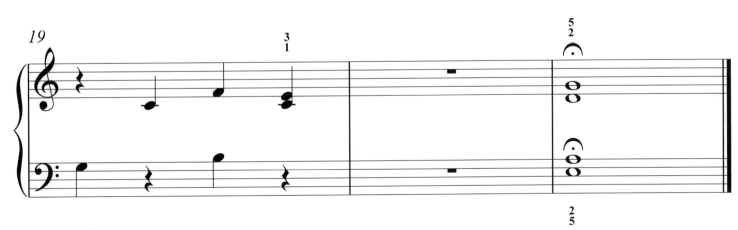

IS YOU IS OR IS YOU AIN'T MY BABY?

Words & Music by Billy Austin & Louis Jordan

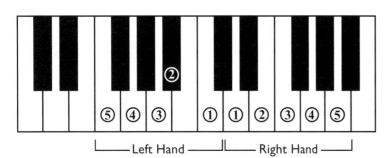

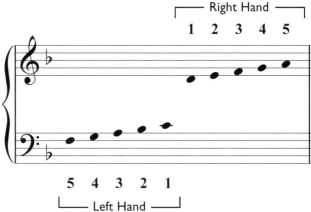

Steady stomp ♩ = 116

Is you is, or is you ain't my ba - by?

The way you're act - ing late - ly makes me doubt.

You is still my ba - by, ba - by.

Seems my flame in your heart's done gone out. A

THE GIRL FROM IPANEMA (GAROTA DE IPANEMA)

Original Words by Vinicius De Moraes, English Words by Norman Gimbel
Music by Antonio Carlos Jobim

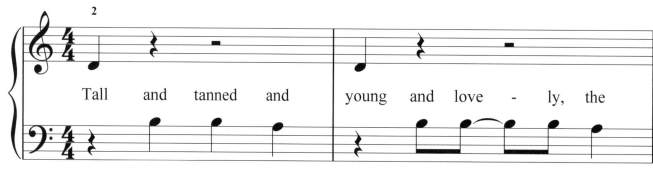

Lazily ♩ = 126

Tall and tanned and young and love - ly, the

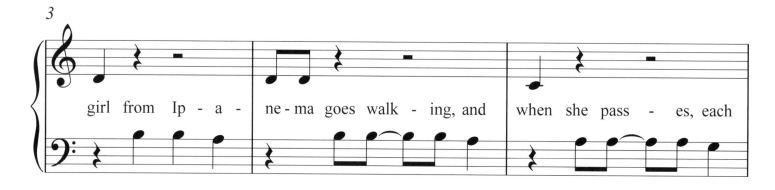

girl from Ip - a - ne - ma goes walk - ing, and when she pass - es, each

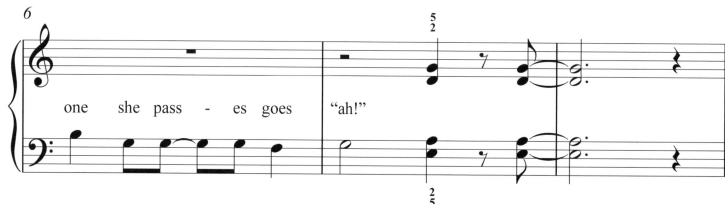

one she pass - es goes "ah!"

123456789

EASIEST 5-FINGER PIANO COLLECTION

ALSO AVAILABLE IN THE SERIES...

Abba
A great collection of 15 classic Abba hits, including 'Dancing Queen', 'Fernando', 'Take A Chance On Me' and 'Thank You For The Music'.
AM998404

Ballads
A superb collection of 15 well-known ballads, including 'Fix You', 'I Have A Dream', 'Let It Be' and 'What A Wonderful World'.
AM995346

The Beatles
15 classic Beatles hits including 'All My Loving', 'Hey Jude', 'She Loves You' and 'Yellow Submarine'.
NO91322

Chart Hits
15 popular chart hits including 'About You Now', 'Bleeding Love', 'Clocks', 'Foundations', 'Shine' and 'Umbrella'.
AM995357

Classical Favourites
15 classical pieces including 'Jupiter' (Holst), 'Lullaby' (Brahms), 'Minuet In G' (J. S. Bach) and 'Spring' (Vivaldi).
AM998393

Film Songs
15 great film songs including 'Breaking Free', 'Don't Worry, Be Happy', 'Somewhere Out There' and 'You've Got A Friend In Me'.
AM995335

Showtunes
15 great showtunes including 'Any Dream Will Do', 'Circle Of Life', 'Mamma Mia' and 'My Favourite Things'.
AM995324

Today's Hits
15 of today's current chart hits including 'Hallelujah', 'Human', 'If I Were A Boy' and 'Viva La Vida'.
AM998415

...PLUS MANY MORE

Published by
Wise Publications
14-15 Berners Street,
London W1T 3LJ, UK.

Exclusive Distributors:
Music Sales Limited
Distribution Centre, Newmarket Road,
Bury St Edmunds, Suffolk IP33 3YB, UK.
Music Sales Pty Limited
20 Resolution Drive, Caringbah,
NSW 2229, Australia.

Order No. AM1001055
ISBN 978-1-84938-610-4
This book © Copyright 2010 Wise Publications,
a division of Music Sales Limited.

Edited by Lizzie Moore.
Arranging and engraving supplied by Camden Music.

Printed in the EU.

Download to your computer a set of piano accompaniments for this *Popular Jazz Standards* edition
(to be played by a teacher/parent).
Visit: **www.hybridpublications.com**
Registration is free and easy.
Your registration code is SH354

Your Guarantee of Quality
As publishers, we strive to produce every book to the highest commercial standards. This book has been carefully designed to minimise awkward page turns and to make playing from it a real pleasure. Particular care has been given to specifying acid-free, neutral-sized paper made from pulps which have not been elemental chlorine bleached. This pulp is from farmed sustainable forests and was produced with special regard for the environment. Throughout, the printing and binding have been planned to ensure a sturdy, attractive publication which should give years of enjoyment. If your copy fails to meet our high standards, please inform us and we will gladly replace it.

www.musicsales.com